MINDFUL
EATING

Mindfulness, the chance to choose.

By Leigh Eastman

'You have to keep going to get anywhere' is a favourite Mantra of mine. What is the alternative? Every journey begins with one single step, this could be your first step to the incredible, amazing, exciting life you were born to live x

FSC

ISBN 978 0 9929690 1 1

Published by Leigh Eastman

About the author

Leigh Eastman has been a successful therapist for over 17 years. During that time she has qualified in 14 complementary therapies. Her greatest passions to date are teaching Pilates and doing massage. She also runs Mindfulness Workshops. She works out of Eden Therapy Centre in Hampshire with her son who is an Osteopath and also a Pilates instructor. Her daughter lives in London and works for the BBC.

Leigh believes that you can create anything you want in your life. She believes you can be who you want to be, have what you want to have but most importantly you can find peace no matter what.

Foreword by Leigh

I have spent much of my adult life battling with my weight

I have spent much of my adult life battling with temptation

I have spent much of my adult life yo yo dieting

| have spent much of my adult life loathing myself

I have spent much of my adult life beating myself up

I have spent much of my adult life comparing myself with others

I have spent much of my adult life looking in the mirror at my stomach

I have spent much of my adult life feeling self-conscious

I have spent much of my adult life dreading holidays

I have spent much of my adult life thinking about food

I have spent much of my adult life smarting at my reflection in a shop window

I have spent much of my adult life exercising

I have spent much of my adult life watching my willpower evaporate.

Then I discovered Mindfulness...

Foreword

I first met Leigh a few years ago – we were both students on a course for therapists.

From the start, it was clear she was head and shoulders above the rest of us. While we saw two or three clients a week in the new technique we were learning – she saw thirty. That alone would have been enough to make us hate her – but her amazing generosity (every single week she brought a big packet of the best, most delicious biscuits in!) and her personality made us love her instead. She's warm, funny, vital and generous. As I got to know her better I realised she had some powerful insights into a better way of living. In the areas of better sexual relationships, better eating and better living, you'll find her mindful approach clear, candid, and life-enhancing. She shares aspects of her own life: all she's learned is condensed into the books, yet with practical techniques that you too can follow. There's nothing glib: she admits her own mistakes, and what she's done to change. I am using some of her ideas in my own life now – and feel so much more alive. You can never have too much love…that's one view I share with Leigh. But first you have to love yourself. Leigh's books aren't just full of wisdom – they're easy to read and funny too. Mindful living isn't heavy or difficult. It will bring you so much joy. And you can get high on life! Read Leigh's books and give it a try. I'm proud to say I helped her a little bit in getting the words down… but the knowledge is all hers. She helped me on a personal journey to happiness – she'll help you too.

Diana Cambridge
www.dianacambridge.co.uk
diana@dianacambridge.co.uk

Dedicated to
the man in the purple shirt...

Thank you to

My kids
for being amazing.

My ex-husband
for being supportive - regardless.

My family
for their belief in me - even when I am madly impulsive.

My friend who is a boy
for helping me become more Mindful.

My men
for their patience with me.

Diana Cambridge
for her guidance.

Leila Coppock
for her inspiration.

My Pilates pupils
for making my classes a joy.

My clients and patients
for their support in a job that I love.

Anyone who has crossed my path
for sharing their lives with me.

Radio 2s Chris Evans
the best tonic for positivity ever.

Phil Fisher
*for all his incredible work. For helping me make my dream
an amazing reality.*

Contents

1. Why do we eat?

Habits
Disordered eating
Listening to your body
Mindful eating

Why do we eat?

'Let food be thy medicine, thy medicine shall be thy food'
Hippocrates

I think in these times of abundance, of being able to get any food under the sun, at any time regardless of the season has contributed to us losing our way when it comes to food. We now seem to be living to eat rather than eating to live. We need food to fuel our bodies, give us energy to do what we have to do and to replenish nutrients needed for cell and organ growth and regeneration.

Food has been so over processed that a lot of the time we are eating 'dead' food, giving us very little in the way of nutrition. I saw a programme recently which showed that you now have to eat 3 carrots to get the same vitamins and minerals as you used to get from one. They found oranges in supermarkets with no nutrients in at all due to the fact that the fruit was picked before it was allowed to ripen in the sun, where nature would have bestowed all the natural ingredients in due course and process.

I have got so much more Mindful over the last few years with regard to eating 'dead' food or food that has been tampered with. Like adding omega oils to bread and spreads instead of eating the foods that naturally contain it. Some time ago my son tried doing the Atkinson diet which meant no wheat. He had one heck of a job trying to find foods that didn't contain wheat, foods that didn't even need wheat. No wonder people are becoming wheat intolerant. not only are they having a wheat based cereal and toast for breakfast, they then go on to have sandwiches for lunch and pasta for tea, and that's without the biscuits and cakes in between.

I just love my first hot drink in the morning – fresh lemon and ginger

Habits

"One should eat to live, not live to eat' Benjamin Franklin

There is also a social side to eating, going out for a meal, having friends round for dinner, breaking bread together. It is one way that we women nurture those we love and care about. I know when my children were little I showed them I loved them by feeding them. I do this still with the men in my life. If there is a particular cake or meal they are fond of then I take great delight in making it for them. - the way to a man's heart is through his stomach. I am as guilty as the next woman for overfeeding those I love but now I limit it to the occasional indulgence as no-one needs to eat as much as we do.

Every celebration and holiday, beit Christmas or Easter leads to over catering and over consumption. Now this on its own isn't terrible, no-one wants to be a party pooper but what has happened is that this over indulgence has become a habitual way of life.

If we go back to the beginning when there were no overstocked supermarkets supplying us with irresistible goodies, too luscious to be ignored. To a time when we had to hunt and forage for food, expend energy in doing so and in living, building shelters and working the land, then we can see how far away from our origins we have come.

I am not suggesting we should all start hunting and foraging but what I mean is that we are expending far less energy now and eating far more calories. We don't even have to go back that far in time to see when things began to change dramatically. After the war when there was rationing and many men had physical jobs and many women scrubbed the floors and did the washing in a machine that wasn't automatic, I have heard it said that this balance lead to it being one of the healthiest periods in time.

I don't deny myself anything, I just go for less of it, less often.

Disordered eating

'When walking, walk. When eating, eat' Zen Proverb

So while we have evolved in terms of food technology and labour saving devices, the scales have been tipped against us, making food availability plentiful and labour saving devices available to everyone. So no wonder we are getting more and more over weight. I am not saying this to be a prophet of doom, I love food and labour saving devices as much as the next person, but we have lost all sense of proportion and awareness. Many of us are now eating for the sake of it and not because we are hungry.

I went on a course recently about disordered eating and eating disorders. Most of which it concluded, was down to issues of emotional imbalance. I have long ago learned that over eating isn't about food. Sometimes it is boredom. I know a couple of retired gentlemen who are now grazing constantly instead of going out to work, they have little round tummies and have trouble doing up their shoes. They have just lost their sense of purpose, so I guess theirs is an emotional issue of sorts also. Most of us overeat in an effort to fill an emptiness within us, or to bury or assuage a long ago hurt or injustice. That is why diets don't work, or the weight doesn't stay off, because firstly it isn't just about food and secondly it doesn't change ones relationship with food.

Seven years ago I was about 4 stone overweight and at 4 foot 10 and three quarters I looked like an oxo cube. I lost the weight and have managed to keep it off. In the beginning though it was a real struggle. I had to exercise my socks off to offset my battle with food. It was only when I started training as a hypnotherapist and started practising Mindfulness that the struggle diminished. I became more conscious that I had a choice. Why did I want to eat? Was I hungry or did I just want to change the way I felt. I work til 9 or 10 pm most nights and when I got in I was like a locust and wanted to eat anything that wasn't nailed down.

I only eat for breakfast, food that excites me.

Listening to your body

'How we prepare our food, how we consume our food really makes a difference in how our food satisfies us and shapes the role we give food in our lives. Is it something we stuff in to satisfy an urge or something we savour to feed us physically and sustain us spiritually?' Mary DeTurris Poust

I wasn't hungry, I was tired. I tried having nothing in the house to tempt me, but it is amazing how creative you can be even when the cupboards are practically bare. The other thing you find is that actually you just like food and eating and that's fine, but then you need to consider quality not quantity. I have come across girls who have been on those liquid diets, feel absolutely deprived and know when they have finished their penance they are going to have a food and alcohol binge. One girl lost 9 stone, went abroad and had plastic surgery, came back and proceeded to put on 11 stone.

It often amuses me when I am doing a consultation with people and they refer to having been bad or good, it is almost like a confessional. Who said that certain foods belong on the good list and others on the bad. I always ask if they enjoyed their 'sin' and if they say yes then all well and good, just forgive yourself and move on. If they say no then I suggest that it was a waste of time, energy and calories. If you choose to eat something, accept it, enjoy it to its fullest and then let it go. When you realise that you have a choice you find yourself making better choices for you. When there are cakes being offered at work on a daily basis, you can choose to say yes or no. If you say yes then eat it Mindfully, savouring every mouthful and then be Mindful at lunch time as to whether you are really hungry or are just eating because you always eat at lunchtime.

If you say no thank you, you will feel pleased with yourself, you will feel motivated by the feelings of positivity you get from making a conscious choice based on your needs at that moment. Then you can really enjoy your lunch or dinner because you are actually hungry. I hate it when I eat something when I am not hungry and it isn't a 'mealtime' because I have ruined it for myself. I can't and won't eat a dinner if I have had something already. For several reasons. One being I won't enjoy it so it is a waste of time and calories. Secondly because I only eat small meals these days my capacity for food has diminished. Gone are the days when I can eat a three course meal. I have ruined it for myself because I can only manage one course or half of two courses.

A lot of the time when I am looking for food in the evening, it is just because I am tired. I am not hungry.

Mindful eating

"Better to eat a dry crust of bread with peace of mind than have a banquet in a house full of troubles' Proverb

So what does Mindful eating mean. The first part of Mindful eating is about being aware of what you are eating. Have you ever reached for the other half of your sandwich only to find you had already mindlessly eaten it and not realised or tasted it? What about putting your hand into that packet of crisps or biscuits only to find it empty - they don't give you as many as they used to do they! Do you continue to eat the whole bar or box of chocolates because you have started it even though you aren't actually enjoying the rest of it. There was something on the television about people in a cinema being given stale popcorn to eat. They ate it mindlessly and were unaware of its quality. The same people were asked to taste it when not engrossed in something else and immediately found it tasted old.

So one thing to try is to be with your food while you are eating it. See it, smell it and taste it. The body assimilates food better when it is savoured and eaten with presence. There is a raisin meditation that is mentioned in several Mindfulness books whereby you have to look at, feel it with your hand and then your mouth - a humble raisin. You then eat it as slowly as you can, taking note of the texture and taste. Then do it again with another raisin. I was amazed, when doing this, to find that each raisin was totally different in texture and taste. Each had its own personality! Previously I had just thrown a handful of raisins into my mouth, chewed detachedly and swallowed.

What happens when you are more Mindful of the eating process is that you don't eat as much because you hear your body saying it is full. You can acknowledge when you have had enough or you can stop before you have cleared your plate because you feel to eat any more is not going to be a pleasure. You have had all you needed and you enjoyed what you had very much. Eating food with good flavours increases satisfaction and improves digestion. As human beings we need a certain amount of gratification, and if we don't get it in quality we tend to make up for it in quantity.

I only own beautiful mugs and cups. Every drink is a nurturing experience.

Improving your relationship with food

Remember the whole point of eating is to keep you alive - to give you energy - to replenish and rebuild.

Dead and processed food is ageing. As often as you can eat fresh food.

Has your relationship with food become a stale tired habit. The body gets used to the same things and does not work as efficiently. Vary your diet.

If you are still feeding and shopping for a family when there are now only two of you. Reinvent your meal times to suit your ever changing lifestyle.

If you are eating more in the way of fuel than you are expending in energy then you need to either increase your exercise or cut down on calories.

There is no magic wand. You have to do the Maths. Unless you are running marathons you really don't need a lot of food.

Listen to your body. Are you really hungry or are you tired, stressed, bored or thirsty.

Whatever you choose to eat, make sure you acknowledge and enjoy every single mouthful. No regrets

Be Mindful of what you are eating. Smell it, see it and taste it. Then you will be satisfied.

Only choose to eat food that excites you.

2. Choices

Friend or foe
Sugar
Yes but...
Excuses

Choices

'Tell me what you eat, and I will tell you who you are'
Brillat-Savarin

The second mindful ingredient is the food you choose to eat. Do you enjoy it? Is it really what you wanted to eat, or are you eating it because of habit, time or boredom? Very rarely do I eat food that I don't absolutely love. I feel it is a waste of my time, effort and most definitely calories. I also feel very cheated if I go out to eat and don't enjoy the food I have chosen. I don't deny myself anything. What you find when you relinquish your sack cloth and ashes approach to food, is that you start to choose life enhancing, nutritious foods because actually these are what delight your palate.

Another thing that I feel is part of the Mindfulness and food issue is presentation. I will talk more about this later, but I just want to say from a Mindfulness point of view, what you see in front of you on your plate is almost as important as what it tastes like. I know of people who are put off by a plate piled high with a mish mash of food. Eating should appeal to many of our senses - be Mindful to smell it, admire it, and then taste it. I guarantee you are on the road to being more than satisfied.

At any stage of the eating process you have a choice and you can make the right choice for you. Firstly you can choose what you buy. You can ask yourself questions as you shop. Is this food right for me? Is it going to help me on the way to who I want to be and how I want my body to be? You know your weaknesses so there is no point buying something just in case. If it isn't a necessary component of your meal plan then don't buy it. I have cut my food bill by three quarters by only buying what I need. The next choice is what you eat and when. Are you hungry? Are you just eating out of habit? Is it a sensible portion size? Have you stopped eating when you are satisfied not stuffed?
Everything is a choice.

If I choose to eat something 'naughty' I jolly well enjoy it and move on.

Friend or foe

'Taken slowly, or mindfully, even eating an orange or a bowl of soup, or a small piece of dark chocolate for that matter can take on the flavour...' Mary DeTurris Poust

Without fail we are told on a regular basis that we should be eating more of something. The next week research shows less of something else is known to be curative or can lead to something else. So what do we believe? The answer is what we want to believe. Those who enjoy a glass of wine rejoice when they read that it is now good for them in moderation. The next month someone else will then decide it's not that good. Those who like their wine, their 'treat', choose to ignore the warnings but the report has taken a bit of the pleasure away, leaving them with a niggling feeling of guilt and leading to the being 'good' being 'bad' scenario.

It's the same with chocolate. You can almost hear the cheer from chocoholics when research finds that it is good for you. You 'cock a deafun' to the rest of the report that says ONE square of 70 percent dark chocolate. The silly thing is that those who are able to listen to their bodies and make conscious choices are only having one square of dark chocolate a day anyway, that is why they are still slim. They say that they eat chocolate but it is not the same as the overweight person eating a chocolate bar daily that has the same calorific content as an evening meal.

We don't have to be paranoid about food, let's face it who has the time, but just by reminding ourselves why we eat in the first place, then trying to make more conscious choices more often than we make unconscious choices. Sometimes it's about educating yourself, sometimes it's about listening to your body and sometimes it's about taking control and caring enough about yourself to feed, nourish and nurture yourself so that you feel the best and healthiest that you could possibly be and forgive yourself for the times when life takes over and it all goes out the window.

My portion size is about a quarter of what it used to be.

Sugar

'Foods high in bad fats, sugar and chemicals are directly linked to many negative emotions, whereas whole, natural foods rich in nutrients - foods such as fruits, vegetables, grains and legumes - contribute to greater energy and positive emotions.' Marilu Henner

We have so lost our way when it comes to food. There is so much out there, so many wonderful choices and so many hidden calories. Did you know that in Japan, refined sugar is known as 'the white poison' and in China it is called the 'great white death'. Sugar overstimulates the pancreas, exhausts the adrenals, leaches minerals from bones and organs, upsets carbohydrate/protein balance, leads to immune weakness and allergies, to name but a few effects. It can also lead to obesity, hypoglycaemia, diabetes, high blood pressure, heart disease. In fact there is quite a long list. Makes you think doesn't it. It can even contribute to memory loss, lack of concentration, nervousness and anxiety. Talk about choose your poison!!!

At the beginning of the year there was a lot of media coverage about the consumption of sugar. How it is now considered worse for the body than fats. How food companies should address the issues. I found that it made no difference to many of my clients. One lady who eats a packet of fruit pastilles a day took no notice of the reports at all. It makes you wonder as to the benefits and relevance of these reports. It also makes you wonder what it will take for people to become more Mindful of what they are eating and its effects.

I know a couple of guys with cancer; one has leukaemia and the other a brain tumour which has not been completely removed. Both of them have incredibly sweet tooth's and both have found from doing their own research that sugar and carbohydrates feed cancers and tumours. In Chinese medicine sweet cravings mean naturally 'sweet' foods not sugar and definitely not processed sugars. It is not going to delight you to know that sweet foods could be carrots, parsnips or sweet potatoes in their skins or even white rice. A sweet tooth could also be satisfied by adding dates or apricots to your porridge while cooking. It doesn't mean you have to give up all your 'pleasures' in life just be Mindful that eating too much of it too often could tip the balance between good long term health and some form of degeneration.

To a great extent I am sugar free. I choose not to include in my diet, something that could be detrimental to my health.

Yes but...

*'The individual who says it is not possible should move out of the
way of those doing it' Tricia Cunningham*

Many people talk to me about their weight problems. They hope
I have a magic wand which will take all responsibility away from them and
they will wake up slim and able to eat whatever they wanted. I suggest
strategies and give explanations but really they are not willing to do or
change anything so they will keep doing what they have always done and
keep getting what they have always got. Actually no they won't get what
they have always got which is a weight problem, it will actually get bigger
and bigger with each passing year.

I was speaking to a lady who was always hungry. I suggested that keeping
eating was encouraging her stomach to produce more stomach acid because
it came to expect a constant supply of food without a break. What your mind
perceives, then your stomach will react to accordingly. I asked her if she was
sure it was hunger and not perhaps thirst or tiredness. No it was definitely
hunger pangs she was feeling and she wasn't open to any suggestions to the
contrary. Why was this? Because she liked to eat. She didn't like having a
weight problem or being the fattest one in her family but it wasn't her fault
that she was always hungry!

When I hear yes but ... then I know that there is resistance to change, advice
and to even acknowledging that the problem is of their own making. No-
one wants to hear that the responsibility for their weight/health/fitness
problem is solely of their own making. They home in on reports of fat genes,
hereditary tendencies, big bones. They leap from one diet fad to another but
none of this works for them. They talk about what they can't do rather than
what they can do.

**I really enjoy being slim. All it takes is choosing between eating
something or not.**

Excuses

'Food is an important part of a balanced diet' Fran Lebowitz

They say I can't change my poor eating habits this week because I am going out to dinner on Saturday so there isn't any point. Then after the dinner on Saturday they might as well have that bacon sandwich on Sunday because the damage has been done. They were going to start changing what they ate on Monday morning but someone brought cakes to work so that day was a right off as well .... And so it goes on. I have known clients who, have come to me for over ten years and in all that time they have been on no end of diets and they are bigger today than they were then.

What a waste of their time and energy. How about just adding a bit of exercise into your schedule I suggest. Yes but ..... I had to go to the dentist after work on Tuesday. .... It rained on Thursday. .... It is almost as if they have tuned their radar to a setting that gives them a reason not to. And so another week, month or year goes by and nothing has improved, the mountain they have to climb just gets taller and steeper. Yes but ... Means I want to moan about it, complain about it but I can't do anything about it, the task is too great.

One of the treatments I do is colonic irrigation. People come for various reasons from constipation to bloating and wind. After the consultation and treatment it is usually obvious as to the reason for their problem. However suggest they change their consumption of something or increase their intake of something else and I am often met with resistance. I just don't understand this mentality. You have a problem... There may be a solution.....why the hesitation. Your choice.

I only eat from small plates and bowls. This outsmarts my greedy eyes.

Improving your relationship with food

Try to remind yourself before you start to prepare your food, why it is you eat. Imagine the food you are preparing doing wonderful things to your body, promoting health and energy.

Whatever you decide to change - just take it one bite at a time - changing or thinking about changing everything at once won't work. Make one change at a time and when it becomes a habit then you can add to it.

Imagine every morning is Monday morning. Forget what you ate or didn't eat yesterday. Start afresh today and don't accumulate 'sins'. The fact that you haven't given up completely is the place from which to start.

Be aware of your food as you prepare it. It might sound a bit 'new agey' but try appreciating the wonder of the food you are preparing, how it grew and what can do for you.

Try and be aware of your input to expenditure ratio. If you are sedentary then you don't need to consume the calories of a marathon runner!

Savour every mouthful of whatever you are eating even if it falls into your 'bad' list - make the choice and then jolly well enjoy it.

You may well find that by eating mindfully that food tastes better than it has ever tasted before, or alternatively you may find that actually you are not enjoying what you are eating so you choose to stop there and then.

Listen to your body, it really can tell you what it needs, when it is hungry and when it is full, when it is tired, when it is dehydrated or even when it needs to move!

As our body is made predominantly of water, why not see if you are thirsty rather than hungry unless of course you are not interested in finding out because then you have one less reason to eat!! Yes but .... I don't like the taste of water....

There are no good or bad foods there are only good or too many bad choices. Try and keep balance and perspective.

3. Greedy eyes

A Portion size
Less is more
Overeating
Changing lifestyles

Greedy eyes

'When it comes to eating right and exercising, there is no 'I'll start tomorrow' Tomorrow is a disease' Terri Guillemets

I remember as a child, my mother feeding the five of us on one small chicken and still having enough meat left over for the next day. I also remember having a fry up for breakfast and then a three course meal for dinner on Christmas and then having room for sandwiches and cake in the evening. These days if I have a fry up for Xmas breakfast I need at least 8 hours before I would be hungry enough to even attempt Christmas dinner and even then it is only the main course and even then I can't eat it all.

So what has happened? Either my stomach has shrunk or the size of our portions has sneakily increased without us noticing it. I think also the size of the plates we are using has grown and we are now eating dinner off of what is essentially a serving plate. So we fill these plates and then we feel obliged to clear same plates of every morsel of food regardless of us having had enough several mouthfuls beforehand. Many of us just eat and eat whatever is put in front of us and that includes the bread in the basket to the side. Why do they do that in restaurants? Give you bread before your dinner, I for one am full up just eating the bread.

I met a guy who had a bit of a weight problem (they always say that, but usually it is more than a bit!). He told me he didn't eat much. What did he eat I enquired ...... well there was cereal and toast regardless of the fact that he may have felt satisfied with one or the other, then he had a large glass of milk and possibly a biscuit, then sandwiches and crisps for lunch, Another glass of milk and then a large salad for dinner. We worked out that in essence he was probably eating nearer 9 meals a day rather than the 3 he told himself he ate. Everyone tells me proudly of the salads they eat, but tend to think that they can put anything with a lettuce leaf, call it a salad and it be virtually calorie free.

By trial and error, I have discovered what foods really hit the spot for me.

Portion size

*'You better cut the pizza in four pieces because I'm not hungry
enough to eat six.' Yogi Berra*

Many of us will have experienced eating in a restaurant when you get served
a small helping of the meal you have chosen and it sits on your plate looking
up at you as if challenging you to feel mentally, emotionally and physically
satisfied by such a paltry amount of food. First you think ... Is that all I am
getting for my money, then you think .... I am still going to be hungry after
that. But actually if you are honest with yourself and you allow yourself the
time to savour your food, you find that surprisingly it was enough.

It is well documented that we only need to eat enough food equivalent to
the size of our cupped hands. Our stomach is only the size of our fist and
not actually the size of the protrusion between our ribs and our pelvis. I
have some small Chinese bowls which I give to people to demonstrate the
portion size. I put my fist into the bowl and there is still room to spare.
However most people are horrified at the prospect of eating so little food.
They think they will die of hunger or pass out because their blood sugar
levels will dip or fluctuate.

How often have you really enjoyed what was on your plate? The whole plate.
The first couple of mouthfuls were delicious ..... but by the time you got to
the final few mouthfuls you were probably just eating it out of habit, almost
mindlessly clearing your plate because it was there. Then afterwards felt
stuffed, bloated and uncomfortable. Surely those last few mouthfuls didn't
warrant the discomfort that followed, not to say the obvious unnecessary
calories and pounds. If you don't have the self- discipline to stop when you
are comfortably replete then putting less on your plate is the obvious choice.

**I prepare enough of my salad bowl to last me three days, which lessens
my thinking and preparing times.**

Less is more

'More you eat, the less flavor; the less you eat, the more flavor'
Chinese Proverb

You can compare your stomach to a washing machine. If you overfill your washing machine it doesn't work as efficiently as it would with just the right size of load. Your stomach is the same, if it is overwhelmed with vast quantities of food it struggles to digest and process the food efficiently. You may live longer if you are underfed rather than over fed. Limiting your intake of food and making informed choices about what you eat can extend lifespan and bring freedom from most diseases such as heart disease and cancer.

The diet industry is huge because people are always looking for an excuse to eat more food. They go on this diet because they can eat what they want 5 days out of 7, or that diet because they don't have to deprive themselves of cakes and biscuits. They can still eat three to five meals a day. And okay sometimes they may lose weight but it is becoming more and more recognised that the weight loss is rarely sustained. Why is this? It's because these diets don't change the dieters relationship with food. It is almost a challenge to see how long they can go without their favourite food before they crumble and succumb.

The couple of clients, who were on liquid diets, managed it for as long as they could, losing quite vast amounts of weight but as soon as they stopped they were down the takeaway shop and in the off licence. They felt so deprived. Subsequently they soon put back on all the weight they had lost and some more. Not only had they not changed their relationship with food, but more importantly they hadn't changed their relationship with themselves. They hadn't learned how to make the right choices about what they ate and still worked on the all or nothing principle. They hadn't trained their greedy eyes.

If I am not really enjoying what I am eating I tend to leave it.

Overeating

*'Personally I don't think the concept of the 'cheat days' works, ...
you don't recommend heroin once a week to a recovering heroin
addict, do you?' Deepak Hiwale*

Overeating and large portion sizes seems to be becoming a worldwide
problem. I was recently in America where, as we all know, the size of a meal
is enormous. Even a half portion salad could easily feed a family of four,
and when you don't eat it all they ask if you want a doggie bag to take it
home. No thank you I never want to see it again! Yet when I was in Bali I
would often see people eating their lunches with chopsticks and the portion
size was the size of cupped hands. I never saw any of the locals tucking into
vast plates of food, yet this is what they offered the tourists, acknowledging
that these visitors expected 'all you can eat' breakfast and lunch buffets.

Why is it that we feel we have to keep eating something just to finish it,
when in actuality we have stopped tasting and enjoying it several mouthfuls
ago. Just one more biscuit, one more sweet out of an extra-large bag or one
more scoop of that ice cream. To eat Mindfully means to eat in awareness
of the flavour of something and give your psyche time to acknowledge when
it feels repleted/satisfied. It is only when one eats from this perspective, that
you will crave less rather than more of something.

Overeating isn't just about food as we know. We may have greedy eyes. We
may have an emotional void that needs filling. We may have got our signals
mixed up and hear feed me, when our bodies are actually saying I am thirsty
or I am tired or I am bored. In actuality no amount of food is going to
make the urge go away. So unless we start being Mindful to the messages
from our bodies, it is going to be difficult to stop the need to over eat.

Practising Mindfulness has lessen my need to eat.

Changing lifestyles

'Gluttony is an emotional escape, a sign something is eating us.'
Peter De Vries

I come across many women who, given the choice, would eat fewer meals, and less food if they were not committed to catering to their families and their partners. Particularly older generations of women who still feel duty bound to cater for and to patterns of eating that, while appropriate for a growing family and working model, are not relevant when older or retired. What, when and why one is eating needs, I feel to be re- examined every decade or so to see if the diet still fits the bill.

What we eat in terms of quantity is only one of the criteria to be re-assessed. When one eats can change over your lifetime from snatched breakfasts or even no breakfast before work to a packed lunch and work day snacks to an evening meal eaten around seven. When lifestyles change then this modus operando may no longer fit. Now this is totally a generalisation. If it suits all parties concerned, no-one is putting on weight, no-one is suffering from digestive problems or any other illness then stick to what you know. If however one or both of you finds your waistband expanding or your health is in decline or you are suffering from increased bouts of digestive discomfort then the first thing to address is what and when you are eating.

I know that my parents eating habits have changed since they have retired. They have however tried to cut out the cooked meal in the evening as they realise that they don't really need that amount of food anymore. But old habits die hard and they found it to be a ritual they were loathe to change. They have adjusted their diet in other ways and also the quantity and quality of the evening meal so as to still enjoy the companionable experience.

I decide what food is best for me. I am not swayed by media reports.

Improving your relationship with food

You don't necessarily have to change what you are eating but you most certainly have to address the portion size. Remember how small your stomach is.

Are you really hungry or are you just producing too much stomach acid out of continually grazing?

Overeating makes your digestion less efficient. Like an overloaded washing machine. Try to stop eating before you feel stuffed.

Trick those greedy eyes by filling up a plate or bowl that is only a quarter of the size from which you normally eat. You won't be sorry and you will have cut your calorie intake dramatically.

Don't deny yourself anything. If you have a cake or a packet of biscuits then count that as one of your meals. Acknowledge that two hours later at lunch or dinner time that you are now not actually hungry so don't eat.

Start being selfish. If you don't need a cooked meal then those members of your family who are capable of catering for themselves need to start doing so. Your first duty is to yourself. If you are fat and unhappy then it will reflect on other areas of your life.

Overeating can lead to ill health. People live longer when they eat less not more.

Your dietary habits of 20 years ago don't necessarily fit the bill today. Reassess what you are eating, when you are eating it and why you are eating it. What you ate when you worked a five day week isn't necessarily what you need to be eating now you are at home more.

Boredom can be the biggest problem for some people. It helps not to have temptation in the cupboard.

If you are starting to get acid reflux, indigestion or bowel problems it could mean that the type of food you are eating doesn't suit you anymore. Change what you eat and you will change how you feel.

4 . Urge surfing - what is it?

Outsmarting yourself
Distraction therapy
Be prepared
Removing temptation

Urge surfing - what is it?

'Mindfulness practices enhance the connection between our body, our mind and everything else that is around us. Mindful living is the key to understanding our struggles with weight and to empowering us to control our weight.' Nhat Hanh

Urge surfing is a term coined by Alan Marlatt as part of a program of relapse prevention he developed for people recovering from addictions to alcohol and other drugs. It can actually be used to help with any addictive or compulsive behaviour, which is particularly relevant for working with eating problems. It resonated with me when I was on the course for disordered eating as I saw it as a useful tool to help overcome the desire to eat when you are not hungry.

It is used to enhance the ability to delay and eventually cease disruptive behaviour. The disruptive behaviour with regard to eating being the impulsive urge to reach for the biscuit tin, or stop and buy a chocolate bar. It distracts you from your habit of heading for the kitchen when you come in from work, or mindlessly accepting the cakes that come round the office in the morning. It highlights the moment when all reason goes out the window and all your willpower and self-discipline dissolves despite your resolutions to the contrary.

Urge surfing from a Mindfulness perspective dilutes the thoughts, feelings or urges which overpower your resolve. Instead of the mental battle going on in your head whereby you argue with the undesirable cravings, thoughts, feelings and urges, urge surfing allows you to reach the peak of your desire and sail right past it without acting upon it. Imagine it like being on a roller-coaster. Your craving for something grows, your mental battle with yourself does nothing to assuage your desire. It peaks, your willpower has gone ....you pause, breath, count to ten ....the urge lessens, the desire passes.

I achieve so much more now that I no longer spend my spare time grazing.

Outsmarting yourself

'Lead us not into temptation. Just tell us where it is; we'll find it.'
Sam Levenson

When we use Mindfulness we stay exposed to our thoughts, feelings or urges for their natural duration, without feeding them or repressing them. The more we struggle with our cravings, the more potent they become. The more attention you give it the bigger and more powerful it gets. It is your choice whether you act upon your urges or not. They are just feelings, they pass, they can be changed. Not by fighting or struggling with them but by seeing them, hearing them and accepting them and then letting them be.

In fact, if we just let an urge be - non judgementally - without feeding it or fighting it then it will crest, subside and pass. Of course they come back again but over a period of time. And each time they come and you don't act upon them they become less intense, less potent and less frequent. You then begin to understand that you don't have to react to every urge you get. You begin to allow yourself to acknowledge the feeling and then make an informed decision about whether it is in your best interest to act upon it or let it pass. Which it will.

It is helpful to create an image or an identity for your urge. Mine is like a space invader, one of those little Pacman creatures. It climbs up a hill as my urge increases, it reaches the top, but it doesn't stop at the peak where I would normally react to my desire. It continues out the other side and down the hill. Imagine your urge as a cute creature. Imagine it ambling up to your craving, pausing and then ambling on by until your urge has diminished.

I have nothing in my cupboards that could tempt me in a moment of weakness.

Distraction therapy

'I don't stop eating when I'm full. The meal isn't over when I'm full. It's over when I hate myself.' Louis C. K.

For many of us, the urge surfing theory is fine in principle. When you read about it, rationalise it, you think, that's okay. I can do that. But when you are struggling with your relationship with food, the urges can be so powerful. They can overcome the strongest of resolves if you are unprepared for them. When you do win the battle, and you have successfully urge surfed then the positive feelings become a motivating force. But if, in the beginning you lose more than you win then you may well become tempted to give it up as another lost cause.

So until you become adept at urge surfing in its own right, why not support it with some distraction therapy. Firstly imagine the urge outside of your body. It could be like a graph on your computer screen or an image on your television, anywhere that is not inside your body. This allows for a degree of emotional space, allowing you some distance from the feelings. Then go and find something else to do. Clean your teeth, unload the dishwasher, put in a load of washing. Sort out that pile of mail. Anything, just to give yourself a breathing space.

Then when you have done it, go back to your image and see if it is still there or if it has peaked and has now diminished. This is brilliantly motivating. Firstly because you have cruised past and overcome an unnecessary craving and secondly you have ticked something else off of your to do list. If you can do this every time you have an urge, imagine how many of those jobs on that endless list you have, will get done. It can even work at work. Just finish that report before you have that cake that was offered. With any luck someone else would have eaten it before you get the chance.

I have found other things to amuse me other than eating.

Be prepared

'He who is of calm and happy nature will hardly feel the pressure of age, but to him who is of an opposite disposition youth and age are equally a burden.' Plato

Now we all know we have the willpower to resist an urge when it is imaginary but when it comes to the crunch it is a whole different ball game. How many times have you gone out to dinner resolving not to have a dessert and then when dinner was over, you had a dessert? Or knowing there were cakes coming round the office for someone's birthday and you had decided you were going to refuse one, but didn't in the end? All these failed attempts only go on adding to your sense of disempowerment.

Why not start the day by writing a list of all the little jobs, chores or even things you would actually like to have time to do. We all have so many things we would like to achieve but most remain undone, hanging over us like a weight. I have achieved so much more since I stopped investing so much of my valuable time in eating unnecessarily. Then when the urge to comfort eat begins to grow, make a deal with yourself to do at least one of the things on your list before you succumb.

You may well find that you get so absorbed in the project that you forget the urge, or even if you don't you will have raised your level of positivity to a degree and may not need the food boost. And finally even if you do grab the biscuit, the negativity surrounding the experience will have lessened because of the task you achieved beforehand. Nothing is a failure. It is only your perspective of the situation that makes it so.

I know Mondays are too busy to eat properly, so I am prepared.

Removing the temptations

'More die in the United States of too much food than of too little.'
John Kenneth Galbraith

When I talk to people about what their downfall is with regard to food. Many of them succumb to things in their cupboards that don't really need to be there. It is all very well urge surfing but it is more testing when there is a packet of Chocolate Hobnobs beckoning to you from the biscuit tin. Or that bag of Kettle Chips is crying out to be opened. Why have you got them in the house? Just in case we have visitors. The kids like them. Sadly these are all just excuses. They are really in there for you.

If you really want to eat consciously and Mindfully then these things should not be in your shopping basket. Even your little urge surfing creature is going to have a hard time marching past its favourite snack. So do yourself a favour. Don't give house room to anything unnecessary. Bin the box of chocolates given to you by your friend. They are not a good friend it they give you chocolates. Then if you really want that bar of chocolate you will have to get in your car and go and get it. Thereby giving yourself time to let the urge pass. If it doesn't then you have the choice as to whether you buy the biggest or the smallest bar in the shop.

I have been known to get in the car and drive to my local shop for a packet of crisps. Struggling with the urge. Only to do a U turn before I got there. I have never regretted those times. They go to confirm that it was just an urge with no rational need. By the time I get back home the desire has gone and I feel very pleased with myself. Had I succumbed I would have felt disempowered, demotivated and fatter than ever.

With every challenge I now know I have a choice.

Improving your relationship with food

Remember your urge to eat is just a thought or a feeling and doesn't necessarily require acting upon.

Delay your reaction to reach for something to eat until you are sure it is actually hunger.

It is only an urge if you have eaten in the recent past. It won't be hunger.

Recognise the difference in your feelings - compare real physical hunger pangs to an emotional habitual desire to eat.

Make yourself a list of things you would like to do or achieve and use this as your distraction. You will be amazed how much you get done.

Do yourself a favour, don't buy anything that is not necessary for meals. My cupboards are bare and so is my fridge to a certain extent. Only buy what you need for your meals.

Create yourself a little creature - your urge surfer and watch them trundle past your desire to eat without pausing.

Before you react to an urge - repeat to yourself 'I have a choice, I have a choice'

Don't beat yourself up if you react to an urge - there is always next time.

The more times you win, the more often you will want to do it, the stronger you get, the better with eating you will get.

5. Chinese perspective

The energetics of food
Your body and food
The 5 elements and you
Listening to your body

Chinese perspective

'If people pay attention to the five flavours and blend them well, their bones will remain straight, their muscles will remain tender and young, breath and blood will circulate freely, the pores will be fine in texture, and consequently breath and bones will be filled with the Essence of life.' Huang Di, Yellow Emperor's Classic of Internal Medicine, 2500BC

Food and its energetics took on a whole new meaning for me when I studied for my Acupuncture degree. So much of what I learnt made so much sense. Not only did the Chinese not overeat, but they are/were Mindful of what they were eating and why. I never feel healthier than when I am eating the right food for my constitution. Whether it is seasonal or just the correct food for my body type, when I eat it I am completely satisfied emotionally, it appeals to my sense of taste and smell, and my digestion loves it.

One of my lecturers suggested that when you eat something that meets all your needs your body sighs and you feel an internal fizz or sparkle. When this happens, your body is more able to digest the food properly. It is used efficiently and does only good, no harm. It is nourishing to the mind, body and soul. When you eat the right type of food you feel a sense of wellbeing. You feel totally nourished.

There are so many things we eat that are contraindicative to our overall health. Not only what we are eating but also how we are eating it. I often speak to women on 'diets' who eat nothing but salads all year round and then wonder why they are lacking in energy, are bloated and still can't lose weight. The Chinese don't advocate raw food. They feel that uncooked food weakens an already over used digestive system by using energy to 'cook' the food in the stomach. This leads to a poor assimilation of food.

I feel very different when I have eaten food that really nourishes me.

The energetics of food

'Above all, take satisfaction in the cooking and joy in the eating. If cooking is no more than time-consuming drudgery and eating nothing better than fear, denial and the observation of dietary guidelines, then we subvert and deny one of the great pleasures of our kind. Enjoy' Elisabeth Rosin

The whole story of the energy of food is long and is a whole book in itself. So here is just a taster of how different foods have different energies and the consequences. In Chinese medicine food is either warming or cooling or neutral. This means that this is the affect it has on the body. So a person suffering from hot flushes should avoid food that is warming as this is like putting petrol on an already smouldering fire.

These warm or cool foods have nothing to do with the temperature of them, more to do with the chemical reaction they elicit in the body. Everything is considered. When and where a food is grown, how it is cooked and how you feel when you eat it. And if for that matter it is the right food for you. There are foods that are considered blood nourishing and I recommend these to most women as many of us are lacking. This perspective is not about anaemia. It is about not having the quantity of blood you need for your body to operate efficiently.

Every food you eat has an effect on the chemical makeup of your body. And all foods will affect different people in different ways. Some people can eat a certain type of food and it will nourish them. For others it will deplete their energies. It can most certainly have an effect on your ability to be able to lose weight. If we constantly eat poor quality food and we fail to receive sufficient nourishment, our bodies will hold onto anything it has, choosing not to eliminate because it will try to salvage nutrition from almost anything.

I take very good vitamin supplements. They help me to keep balanced.

Your body and food

'Unquiet meals make ill digestion' Shakespeare

Not only is our body affected by what we eat, it is affected by how we feel, when we eat and what time of day we are eating. Did you know that your digestion is strongest in the morning and weakest in the evening? So what do many people do - skip breakfast and eat the most at the end of the day. Many studies have shown that eating breakfast gives us the best chance of regulating our weight, avoiding diabetes and managing our energy levels throughout the day.

I come across many people who screw their noses up when I mention eating breakfast, but the message here is that distributing nutrients and calories more evenly through the three meals of the day and both reducing the quantity and lateness of the evening meal is pivotal in supporting our health. I would suggest that some people are unable to eat breakfast because the time and size of the evening meal means it is probably still sitting in their digestive system.

An overburdened digestive system becomes sluggish and is unable to keep pace with detoxification and elimination. Encouraging the difficult habit of stopping before we are full and ensuring we eat sufficient foods high in energy, live foods not processed and dead, will support the health of the digestive system. Finally how you feel when you are preparing food and eating it will affect the taste of the food and what your body can do with it. If you are stressed and hurried and absently scoff down your food your body will react to it differently than if you are calm, peaceful and present and not racked with guilt.

I usually sit in my swinging wicker chair by the window to eat my breakfast. It makes for a complete experience and a lovely start to the day.

The 5 elements and you

'The doctor of the future will give no medicines, but will interest his patients in the care of the human frame, in diet , and in the causes of disease' Thomas Edison

In Chinese medicine there are 5 types of people. Wood, Fire, Earth, Metal and Water. Each Element as they are called is associated with organs and flavours. Wood is associated with the Liver and Gallbladder and the flavour is Sour. Fire is associated with the Heart and Small intestine and the flavour is Bitter. Earth is associated with the Stomach and Spleen and the flavour is Sweet. Metal is associated with the Lung and Large Intestines and the flavour is Pungent. Water is associated with the Kidneys and Bladder and the flavour is Salty.

A balanced diet includes all flavours and a wide variety of foods. An excess of one flavour or one type of food can also create an imbalance. Flavours and temperatures are chosen to maintain harmony in the body. The balance will differ according to each person's needs. If a person is suffering from a Lung related condition then foods that have a Pungent flavour would help to regain the health of that organ. I am a 'Wood' person so foods that hit the spot for me are Sour. When I eat something that my body needs I feel differently than when I eat something that is either not conducive to my good health or is in excess of what I need.

Daverick Leggett's book 'Recipes for Self-Healing is a wonderful place to start if you are interested in a different perspective. I use many of his recipes as they are simple to produce and appeal to my sense of taste and wellbeing. Once you begin to understand that there is more to food than meets the eye it will have an effect on you as it did me. Knowing that a certain type of food can help you to regain your health or that too much of another food will be detrimental to your health allows you to understand at another level just what you are putting in your mouth.

I am loathe to eat food that is not nourishing and life giving.

Listening to your body

'Eating three grains of rice with full consciousness, chewing them carefully and extracting every element of nutrition may be just as nourishing as grabbing a sandwich as we rush from one meeting to another' Sandra Hill

If reducing the amount of food you eat is going to be beneficial it must be balanced by ensuring that the quality is there. Being Mindful of the quality of your food - whether it is organically grown, whether it has been processed in any way, how fresh it is will have an effect on our health. Getting the balance right will help you be more satisfied with the food you are eating and its flavour. Eating food with good flavour increases satisfaction and improves digestion.

When you understand that your sweet craving is for energetically sweet foods such as sweet potatoes not chocolate and that your cravings for sweet foods will diminish when you listen to your body then you will begin to restore harmony to your life. When you feel tired at 4 pm in the afternoon and you grab a packet of crisps rather than taking time out to just rest or meditate or have a drink you are not listening to your body. Not every emotion we feel is silenced by food. Those that can be will only react to the right food.

So the next time you feel compelled to reach for something to satisfy a need in you, you may just like to pause, listen to your body - is it hungry, or thirsty or tired? Is there an emotion present and does it require action? If you decide that food is the answer then again pause, what type of food would best suit the need. Will it nurture you energetically and nutritionally because if it doesn't it won't be long before your body is calling out again.

I refuse to beat myself up for the odd slip up. I can start again from now.

Improving your relationship with food

There is more to food than meets the eye. Every food has its own energy. If you are Mindful of what a certain food is doing for your body then you can begin to make the choices you need for good health.

From a Chinese perspective - if you eat seasonal foods that are grown in your own country you will be giving your body the nutrients it needs when it needs them.

If you continually eat food that is lacking in nutrients your body will store everything you eat making it harder for you to lose weight.

The Chinese perspective encourages the cooking of food - lightly so that valuable energy isn't wasted on starting the digestive process.

Your food will be digested better if you eat it slowly, consciously and in a peaceful frame of mind.

Don't be scared to eat breakfast. The right breakfast won't lead you to binge for the rest of the day.

If you eat the same thing for breakfast or lunch day in and day out your body will get bored and won't bother to digest it as well. Variety ensures you get a good range of vitamins and minerals.

Too much of anything can lead to symptoms of ill health. Like wheat for example, wheat based breakfasts, lunches and dinners can cause an overload leading to wheat intolerances - bloating or even Coeliacs disease.

You will know when you have eaten the right food for you when you get a sense of satisfaction from it. A sense of wellbeing that lasts.

Start listening to how your body feels after you have eaten something - is it a good feeling or an uncomfortable one.

6 . Hypnotherapy

Lightening the load
Calm and control
One size fits all
I think therefore I am

Hypnotherapy

"You use hypnosis not as a cure but as a means of establishing a favorable climate in which to learn." Milton Erickson

Hypnotherapy is not about losing control of yourself or turning into a chicken every time someone clicks their fingers! It is about overcoming your negative inner critic and allowing your positive intelligent brain to get back in control. We have two parts to our brain - the primitive negative brain, rather like an overprotective mother who brings up all the bad stuff in the misguided belief that constantly being remind of all your failings, of what can go wrong - will keep you safe. Or it is like a spoilt child who will keep on until it gets its own way.

You may at certain times of the day, have the willpower to resist temptation. However your primitive brain is always on the look out for chinks in your armour. Like a child in the supermarket queue, it will keep on until you relent. It will come up with all sorts of reasons why you deserve that cake, that chocolate bar, that packet of crisps. It knows when you are likely to give in - when you are tired, when you have got stressed, when someone has been mean to you.

What hypnotherapy does is increase your control. Increase the strength of your positive intellectual brain. The part of your mind which knows that actually succumbing will not ultimately make you feel better. That the quick fix will eventually lead you to liking yourself less and making you more overweight than before. It is a struggle for power between good and bad. Like weighing scales - positive experiences and feelings strengthen the power of the intellectual brain and negative feelings and disempowerment strengthens the power of the primitive brain.

Practising Meditation has made me more accepting and calm in every area of my life.

Lightening the load

'The mind is powerful and you have more control than you think'. Scott D Lewis

Imagine your life is like a cardboard box that you carry around with you all the time. Positive feelings, experiences that empower you and make you feel happy lighten the weight of the box. Negative thoughts, feelings and experiences keep getting added to the box. If you fill the box more than you empty it then eventually you will have to put it down - that is when your stress levels increase and it feels like overload. Then you reach for the comfort food.

Hypnotherapy puts you in a relaxed state. A state where your subconscious mind, your intellectual mind is in control. We mistakenly feel that if we relax then our world will crumble around us, nothing will get done. We will sink. Where actually it is only when we are relaxed that things get done easily and effortlessly. It is only then that we are actually in control. It is then that we don't overeat, comfort eat or make food choices that are not in our best interest.

So many women I know feel guilty about doing anything for themselves. They would not dream of taking any time out to just relax, find some peace. They have a list of things to do, a never ending list. They are worn out. They can't stop otherwise what will happen.
I suggest that if they give themselves permission to do something for themselves before they tackle any of their chores, they will find they do them in better spirits because they have nurtured themselves first. Their intellectual brain knows this makes sense but their primitive brain keeps them on the same old guilt trip.

Only I get to choose what is right for me.

Calm and control

'Never be in a hurry; do everything quietly and in a calm spirit.
Do not lose your inner peace for anything whatsoever, even if
your whole world seems upset.' Saint Francis de Sales

I found out quite early on in my hypnotherapy training that 'me' time was invaluable. The sense of peace and calm I got from even five minutes of hypnotherapy was amazing. And I can tell you I was not a calm and controlled person back then. I thought being calm and accepting was for the fairies, not someone who had stuff to do. The relaxed state I achieved gradually began to heal the void inside me that I thought was a constant need for food.

I started to find that being relaxed about life enabled me to get more done and to do it well. You don't realise that being in a constant state of angst is not only exhausting but it also contracts the body. Hence the tension in your neck and shoulders. The gritted teeth. The bad night's sleep. We tend to look outside for things to blame for these feelings when in fact it is all in our heads. Nothing will affect you as much when you are relaxed. When you feel in control you don't have to do things at a hundred miles an hour. You will have faith in yourself.

Over eating is not about food. It is about a lack of control. If you feel out of control in any one area of your life it will overflow into others. I am sure, like me, when you are in control of your eating then other areas of your life appear to be going well also. You have time to exercise. You get all your jobs done. People seem nicer. However when you don't feel you have control over any aspect of your life you start comfort eating, you can't find the time to go to the gym, everyone is getting at you. What changed? It can't be everything else. It must be your internal state.

Sometimes I meditate or sit quietly instead of eating.

One size fits all

'Remain calm, serene, always in command of yourself. You will then find out how easy it is to get along.' Paramahansa Yogananda

I practise solution focus hypnotherapy. I don't tell people what they should or shouldn't be doing. I just try to get them into a relaxed state so that their intellectual brain can be heard. And when you are in a relaxed state you will come up with the solutions to your own problems. We feel it is not helpful to keep going over your problems, your faults. In essence all this is doing is giving your primitive brain a voice. It is an ego maniac. It loves to be heard.

It doesn't matter what you think your problem is. What the reasons are for your acting and reacting the way you do. When you get off your hamster wheel once in a while you will come to find that only you have the answers to making your life the best it can possibly be and that definitely includes your relationship with food. It is not helpful to constantly fixate on your eating habits. Your struggle to control and restrict your diet. The harder you try, the more effort you put into it, the less likely you are to succeed especially if it feels like a chore. If you feel like you are being deprived.

I was treating someone once for an issue with regard to food. He was surprised at how relaxed he felt after one treatment. He asked if we could address his phobia of needles once we had cured him of his first complaint. I told him that I wasn't 'curing' him of anything I was just helping him relax enough for him to act rationally to his problem. A couple of weeks later he came for a treatment and told me that he had been to give blood on several occasions of late and each time the experience improved. He was amazed to discover that it was only his thoughts about anything that he had to fear, not the experience itself.

Being calm, peaceful and relaxed helps me to make all the right decisions.

I think therefore I am

'Life is ten per cent what you experience and ninety percent how you respond to it' Dorothy Neddermeier

We really don't realise how powerful our minds are. Our inner critic keeps us repeating negative patterns of behaviour over and over again on the premise that what we know is safer for us than the unknown. I have lost count of the number of times people say to me - oh I don't like that, I can't do that, or I never do that. You will believe anything if you hear it often enough. What we don't realise is that by thinking like this, we are limiting our options and experiences, and our potential to grow.

I don't like water. I don't like vegetables. I need more than that to eat or I feel sick. We are all big boned in our family. I don't have time to exercise. I am useless. I can't stick at anything. Diets don't work for me. I never eat breakfast. I'm too old to change now. I have never been flexible. I have never been able to touch my toes. I have to have coffee in the morning......... The excuses are endless and are a figment of your imagination. None of the above was you when you were two.

There is nothing I won't try. I don't inwardly criticise myself as I know it is disempowering. If I can't think anything positive, I will think nothing. Negative thoughts and feelings turn into little worms. And the little worms inside you, like inside an apple will keep nibbling away at your confidence, leaving you doubting yourself. So as the years go by the whole amazing person that you are, were, becomes a hollow shell of self- doubt and self-loathing. And all for what? A negative thought.

I now know that eating doesn't make me feel better about how I am feeling.

Improving your relationship with food

You will only be in control of your life when you feel calm and relaxed.

Feelings of being overloaded will always diminish your willpower.

Regular periods of relaxation are an investment in good health. The less time you feel you have for it the more you actually need it.

When you are relaxed you have the mental capacity to make the right choices for you.

Regaining control over any one area of your life will improve your life as a whole.

It doesn't take a lot of time to meditate, just three to five minutes a day could be enough to clear out some of the unwanted clutter that is adding to your life overload.

Stop criticising yourself. Don't talk negatively about yourself. It is disempowering.

Hypnotherapy isn't about changing your personality. It is about letting the true wonderful person that you are, shine.

Consistency is the key. Make a date with yourself. Give yourself permission to jump off of the hamster wheel that is your life every now and then. You will find that you want to jump back on with renewed enthusiasm.

Being a martyr is counterproductive. When you don't nurture yourself your feelings of resentment grow like lime scale. This influences the choices you make.

7. Why I was overweight

My emotional need for food
What works for me
My Mindful eating
Why I love exercise

Why I was overweight

'No man in the world has more courage than the man who can stop after eating one peanut'. Channing Pollock

I have always had a healthy interest in food. I remember my brother and I fighting over our little sister's leftover baby food. But we were never overweight as children. Perhaps one of the reasons was that there wasn't the vast amounts and variety of food available as there is these days. And we weren't drip-fed sweets. They weren't given daily and we saw them as a treat rather than part of our daily intake of food. I guess being children of the 60s and 70s we were allowed out to roam the streets and growing up in New Zealand we had quite an outdoorsy life. So having a good appetite was balanced with exercise.

It was only really when I got married and wanted to love my husband with food that I started to get a weight problem. I was quite into exercise and played squash, went to the gym and did step classes. But unless you are a marathon runner there are very few people whose exercise timetable can outweigh their over consumption of calories. One of my greatest weaknesses is crisps, and a small bag would never suffice. I had the appetite of a locust and so it wasn't long before my four foot ten inch frame got 'stocky'!

One thing I think we women do wrong is to eat the same quantities of food as our men. I know of many women who wouldn't actually bother with as much or as many meals as they do if it wasn't for the fact that their partners demand catering for, morning, noon and night. When I look back on the size of our portions, you could have fed a small country with what we put away. I yoyo dieted for many years but was mainly overweight.

I have broken the cycle of my hating myself so I eat, and eating and then hating myself. My emotions and my eating are now unconnected.

My emotional need for food

'I think sometimes what happens is that all of this feeling out of control manifests itself in trying to control your body; whether it's an eating disorder or talking about getting your nose fixed, as if that's going to be the solution to all the pressure.' Susan Sarandon

The other thing that contributed to my weight gain was the gradual decline of my relationship with my husband. We all know about or have heard of comfort eating, using body fat as a means of self-protection. I was fat and angry, and the angrier I got with myself then the more I hurt myself with overeating. The thing about this is, it is a vicious circle, I ate to improve my mood but it either didn't work or didn't last. On the occasions that I was successful in losing weight I had to really over exercise and log everything I ate so hadn't changed my relationship with food or myself as I soon ate my way back to fatness.

Finally one Christmas about seven years ago I decided enough was enough. Three months later I had shed my weight and to a degree my husband. It was however still down to lots of exercise and a daily struggle with food, particularly in the evenings when I would finish work and go straight to the kitchen to devour anything and everything thus undoing all my hard work and deprivation of the day. What I wasn't acknowledging was that I was tired or thirsty and not hungry.

My other pitfall was a common dieters dilemma - that of being 'good' all week and losing weight (I know I had because I weighed myself every day at least once) and then letting loose at the weekend and putting it all back on again. I would go into a supermarket on a Saturday and deny myself nothing .... crisps, chocolate, alcohol, anything and everything. I would sit and eat the lot on Saturday night then get on the scales Sunday morning dreading what I had done. But it didn't at that stage stop me doing it again and again and again.

There is no food on earth that makes me feel as good as I feel when I buy a pair of size 6 jeans.

What works for me

'I eat an avocado every day. It's amazing for your skin. It's one of the super-foods, and I'm just so into eating properly and healthily.' Joan Collins

So during these last seven years, I have managed to maintain my weight loss but it was always like paddling up stream. Every day a challenge, every day hours of exercise, eating something I deemed 'bad' then jumping on the scales to see if I had undone all the hard work. I was nowhere near the bad place I had been in my previous life but there was still that daily obsession with what to eat, what not to eat and then the post mortem at the end of the day with the subsequent praise or derision.

One thing that helped keep me to get where I wanted to be, was training to be a Pilates teacher. Firstly I didn't want to be overweight to teach as this isn't very inspiring. And secondly it helped tone my body without the constant slog of putting myself through daily exercise to the point of exhaustion. Unlike other forms of exercise that I did, where I would either haul myself out of bed at the crack of dawn or spend hours cycling round the countryside, I was able to incorporate Pilates into my everyday life and really feel the benefits.

The other thing that has got me to where I am today and help keep me there is hypnotherapy. Even while I was training to be a hypnotherapist I began to notice a difference in my relationship with food. Instead of driving the two hours home from Bristol eating constantly, I would think, actually no I am not hungry and so didn't eat. In the past I would have had a big bag of crisps and chocolate to see me through, even though I had had lunch and definitely wasn't hungry. I found that I wasn't having that constant need or craving for food. I could actually say to myself that I wasn't hungry, I was tired or thirsty and address that.

I don't run marathons every day so I don't need to eat as if I did.

My Mindful eating

'Eating properly is great. I mean you cut the fat down, cut the cholesterol out, but still you got to get your rest and you got to have some form of exercise.' Mike Ditka

Finally I found Mindfulness and this appears to be the final piece of my jigsaw. So while Pilates has helped me to get a good body shape without the slog and hypnotherapy has helped to close the emotional gap, Mindfulness has made me aware of what I am eating and why I am eating and given me a useful tool to replace the odd moment of snacking. Instead of the grazing I would sometimes do between clients, I now sit and 'meditate', clearing my head of all the white noise and making room for positive stuff.

I am by no means a saint in the food department, I still love food but now I am more selective about what I eat, and my cravings are more towards 'healthy' nourishing foods rather than 'junk' food. Even now if I do succumb to crisps I rarely have a big bag and if I do I don't eat all of them. I am listening to my body and acting accordingly. There is nothing more motivating than feeling that you have a choice and using that choice to nurture and nourish yourself and then see and feel the results.

There are always going to be moments when I slip back into my old patterns of behaviour but I won't stay there and I will be aware of learning from the experience. I will also be kind to myself when I do trip up and not berate myself or take it out on others. I refuse to feel guilty about sometimes making a less wise choice with food because I know now how to make the right choices more often than not. By continuing to be Mindful when it comes to food I intend enjoying every mouthful of every meal, every day.

I love coming in from exercising in the morning, having a shower and eating my scrambled eggs, mushrooms and tomatoes. I always feel nurtured by it.

Why I love exercise

'Nothing lifts me out of a bad mood better than a hard workout on my treadmill. It never fails. Exercise is nothing short of a miracle.' Cher

Okay so I know exercise is a bit off track when it comes to 'mindful' eating and I did read somewhere that being overweight is 80% food, 10% exercise and 10% genes. However in these days of labour saving devices, cars and television, exercise is a necessary evil. You may find as I did that controlling your eating loses the weight but if you don't do some exercise then that loose untoned skin and body may throw you back into the arms of the Cookie Monster.

I teach Pilates to a wide age range from 15 to 90 and it is a delight to see almost everyone becoming better in their skin. They become more flexible, toned and gain confidence. Some have even gained height due to improved posture. I have two 89 year olds who can now get up off the floor when they couldn't previously. It doesn't matter what form of exercise or movement you take as long as you move. Otherwise you seize up and grind to a halt. I know personally I have never felt so fit and healthy in my whole life.

I know not everyone likes to get hot and sweaty, I do. I don't exactly love running but for a while I would walk everywhere until eventually walking wasn't enough. Then I would jog and walk and then I started running. I can't say that it is my greatest pleasure in life but there is no feeling like coming back to your front door after a run, so glad you bothered. I really enjoy most forms of exercise and while I could survive on just Pilates I like the variety and challenge and the outdoors. I feel I won't get bored or injured if I vary what and when I do things.

Not a day goes by that I don't exercise in one form or another. I feel rusty if I don't.

Improving your relationship with food

Whatever your reasons for overeating are or were, let them go. They are not who you are now and not who you want to be in the future.

There will be a way for you, it is just a matter of looking for the right path. You have to keep going to get anywhere.

Don't fill your plate to the same extent as your partner. You probably only need a quarter of what is on your plate.

Negotiate days when you don't have to cater for anyone but yourself.

The more unhappy you are with any aspect of your life the less inclined you will be to control your consumption of comfort food. If you can change one thing, everything will change. If you don't then you will always struggle with eating.

Changes can be as simple as buying a smaller size of chocolate bar or packet of crisps. It is a start.

Be inventive. I make pizza out of a pitta split in two and smeared with pesto, some vegetables and a sprinkle of parmesan. Delicious.

Life will always have its challenges, but how you react to them is more pertinent than what they are.

Always look for reasons to be in control of your eating, rather than looking for excuses to eat.

Exercise is not synonymous with eating alone, it is for the purpose of keeping your body working, flexible and healthy.

8. Actually - It's not about food

So what are your triggers?
So are you really hungry?
Healthier feelings
It is your choice

Actually - It's not about food

*'The only thing that will make you happy is being happy with
who you are, and not who people think you are.' Goldie Hawn*

So we have seen that actually your unhealthy relationship with food, isn't actually about food, or being hungry. It is about trying to quell negative feelings and emotions for the most part. No-one who is in a calm unstressed frame of mind consciously chooses to eat when not hungry. When we are feeling calm, positive and in control we make positive healthy choices about what we put into our mouths. It only takes the smallest amount of unhappiness or for you to feel tired or thirsty for the primitive spoilt brat part of your brain to start whining for the sweeties.

How often do you touch your stomach before or after you have eaten something? I know I do this often. Especially if I know I have made the wrong food choice or I am about to. We have become consciously and subconsciously obsessed with our weight, our shape, our size. But we are not getting any slimmer or happier as a result. We need to change our relationship with it by changing our relationship with ourselves. We need to stop beating ourselves up because we are less than perfect.

I used to weigh myself morning, noon and night to make sure that I have not put on any weight. Or to check that I have not put on too much weight because of what I had just devoured. I have not weighed myself for a couple of years now because I don't need confirmation of what I have done. I feel secure in the knowledge that for the most part I am eating the quantity and quality of food that is right for me. Weighing myself never helped me make better choices. It was out of fear that I weighed myself. I was scared that I would put on weight.

I am not a martyr when I go out to dinner. I eat what attracts me and I choose to enjoy it.

So what are your triggers?

'The only way to get rid of temptation is to yield to it... I can resist everything but temptation'. Oscar Wilde

So what are your triggers? What exactly makes you reach Mindlessly for the biscuit, crisps or chocolate bar? We all know when we wake up in the morning that we are going to stick to our diet today. Every Monday morning is going to be the day that changes our lives. From this moment on we are not going to have that extra helping of food, not going to eat the kids leftovers, not going to eat as much as our partners. Then we make it through the morning. Make it through lunch being 'good'. Then wham! Like a puff of smoke our resolve disappears.

What is it that happened? It's not your fault, you can't help it. Before you know it you have polished off those four hot cross buns that you resolved only to eat one of when you brought them. But it happens every time. You know the consequences but when it comes to the crunch you conveniently forget them. You forget that you will be racked with guilt afterwards. You forget that you will get on the scales scarcely daring to look just in case you have put on a couple of pounds as a result. How hopeless do you feel? How much more do you loathe yourself?

The thing is, it is only a feeling that is making you react in this way. The more control you have over your feelings the better choices you will make. Give yourself permission to think and feel the way you do but you then don't have to act on it. Remind yourself that when you get these feelings you do this - eat thick doorsteps with butter and jam on, eat peanut butter out of the jar. Acknowledge that the feeling is your trigger and that it can be changed. Mindfulness can help you manage your feelings rather than your feelings managing you. Remember it is only a feeling and a feeling can be changed given the chance and not being immediately reacted upon. Remember the Chapter on Urge Surfing.

I can't be trusted with a jar of peanut butter so I don't buy it.

So are you really hungry?

'Rice is great if you're really hungry and want to eat two thousand of something.' Mitch Hedberg

We women, and possibly a lot of men now, have become obsessed with food. With what we can eat and what we shouldn't be eating. Some of the pleasure has gone out of it as a result. Eating now has an emotional aspect. We feel pleased if we have stuck to the right type of food and portion size. We are racked with guilt and self-loathing if we have eaten something we deem 'bad'. I feel we have lost all perspective. Food, feeding, eating, shopping for food, planning for meals has taken up quite a large percentage of our day.

I know when I started being more in control, I was amazed at how much more free time I had. My food bills were less. The amount of time I spent cooking and preparing and washing up lessened also. I know it is easier for me these days as I have only myself to cater for. It can be so much more of a challenge when you have a family to feed. There are so many more temptations. But I often hear people say that the biscuits and crisps are in the cupboard for the kids. I would ask if they really need to be there. But also when you are coming from a place of calm, control and Mindfulness the temptation lessens.

If you do nothing else other than pause before you put something in your mouth. If you then ask yourself 'Am I really hungry or do I just want to change the way I feel' from tiredness, worry, stress, thirst or just for a bit of me time then you will be on your way to regaining the control over your eating. You will be able to improve your relationship with food so that you are in control of the food, it is not in control of you.

Practising Mindful meditation has increased my Willpower.

Healthier feelings

'First, I eat healthy; it comes from the inside out. If you eat right, your skin, hair, nails will look good. The same if you have negative thoughts - they can give you a bad look, too; we reflect what we eat and think. We also taste and smell what we eat. Being happy and doing what I love really reflects.' Kate del Castillo

It must be so hard for many of us to have good feelings about ourselves when we are being bombarded with images of perfect people. People who look effortlessly lovely, who do everything well. Sail through life without stress or worry. We end up thinking we can never look like that, be like that, so in the end we give up even trying. I personally have learned, with Mindfulness, to shrug off any feelings of competition. I don't compare myself to anyone else. I used to. I admire long legs. Nice hair. But now without jealousy.

We all have our own uniqueness. If we look for people who are better than us we will always find them. And we will always be unhappy because of it. If you look for competition you will find it. We are all beautiful in our own ways. I tend to look for something that is attractive in everyone I meet. I have learnt that by comparing ourselves to other people we will always come up short. The only reason we do this is to try and make ourselves feel better because we are feeling less than our best.

When we start to be in control of our lives. When we start to shrug off our negative feelings then we will lose the need to compare ourselves with other people. I am doing the best with what I have got and who I am. When you start to have a healthy relationship with food you will start to like yourself and it stops mattering what anyone else is doing, being or having. I know when I start to feel inadequate about myself because of other people; I acknowledge that I am probably feeling less than confident for some reason. I then remind myself about what is good about me. What my positive qualities are and I focus on something for me.

I try not to eat on the run as I am not always Mindful of what I have eaten. And I am fed up with crumbs in the car.

It is your choice

> 'To be always intending to make a new and better life but never to find time to set about it is as to put off eating and drinking and sleeping from one day to the next until you're dead'. Og Mandino

So are you going to spend the rest of your life stuck in this rut of self-deprecation. This vicious cycle of eating, berating and hating yourself. Or is this the day you wake up and say I am not doing this to myself anymore. Minute by minute, day by day I am going to consciously choose to do things that are only good for me. I am going to choose to eat food that excites me and that will support me in my quest for health, vitality and a good body image.

You need to start treating yourself like you would treat your most beloved people. You need to care about yourself, put yourself first so that you are not driven to grabbing something for a quick fix. This will only increase your sense of lack. It doesn't take much for our souls to be fed. Just five minutes a day, sat staring out of the window, savouring that cup of hot milky coffee that you so enjoy but usually drink absentmindedly. Then with renewed energy and enthusiasm you will leap into life. You then won't feel compelled to reach for that sugar hug because you have already nurtured yourself.

If you choose to start living your life Mindfully - choosing what you put in your mouth, choosing what comes out of your mouth, choosing what to hold onto in your head, choosing to let go of negative thoughts, choosing only to have in your life things that are good for you, very soon you will begin to achieve everything effortlessly. Your Mindless lack of control over food will be a thing of the past. All negative feelings and thoughts you had about food will dissolve, disperse and disappear and you will then have a healthy relationship with food. So what are you waiting for ......

The less I eat junk food, the less I enjoy it.

Improving your relationship with food

Slow down, stop worrying, enjoy your food

If you can change how you react to just one thing then things will improve.

Know yourself, know your triggers. Relax - the solution will come to you.

There are very few things we don't have a choice about - what we eat, why we eat and when we eat are not things we have no choice about.

You can choose to carry on with your battle with food as you have done for years or you can choose to improve your relationship with food by practising Mindfulness.

Be Mindful of what you eat

Be Mindful of why you want to eat

There is no excuse for carrying on the way you do. Listen to what you say - is it just an excuse.

Negative thoughts and feelings will keep you trapped in the place you are in now. Be Mindful of what thoughts go round and round in your head.

Food is a wonderful, glorious gift - time to start enjoying it.

9. A healthy body

Life balance - work, rest, play, eat and meditate
Middle aged spread
Going forward
A Mindful Future

A healthy body

'If a man achieves victory over this body, who in the world can exercise power over him? He who rules himself rules over the whole world.'
Vinoba Bhave

If I don't exercise for a couple of days due to long working hours or other commitments I begin to feel stagnant and rusty and don't feel I have the same appetite for food and life. I know they say exercise three times a week but I think this is just an opt out clause for reluctant movers. I advocate some form of exercise and movement every day. We were designed to move, to stretch and to get our blood flowing and our bodies oxygenated. AND the more you move the more calories you burn and so the less likely you are to gain weight.

I don't care what age, shape or size you are, if you are still breathing there is some form of exercise you can do. If you don't enjoy it you won't do it and you definitely won't keep it up so you may need to try a few different things before you find what suits you. I incorporate exercise into my daily routine in the same way as I do cleaning my teeth or having breakfast. It is an immovable part of my timetable, a regular appointment that I keep just as I would a hair or dentist appointment. I never look for excuses not to do it. If it is raining I workout indoors, if its dry I go out. I don't wait for Spring when it's only Autumn.

I intend still doing some form of exercise until I die. I intend still teaching Pilates until then also. Joseph Pilates was still fit and vital in his 80s. I have a lady of about 83 in one of my classes who can do sit ups, push ups and roll overs better than a lot of women half her age, because she never stopped because 'she was too old'. I always make time and I work 13 hours a day and every day of the week but it is probably because I exercise that I can.

I have now found that I don't have to exercise to exhaustion to get positive results.

Life balance - work, rest, play, eat and meditate

'The way you think, the way you behave, the way you eat, can influence your life by 30 to 50 years.' Deepak Chopra

What I have found since becoming more Mindful is that although I choose to incorporate a lot of different things into my life I am able to get a better balance than I used to. I find that I am getting as much if not more done by slowing down, taking time for myself and being peaceful. I used to turn my nose up at calm measured people, thinking they obviously didn't have enough in their lives or they weren't trying hard enough. I felt I was only half living if I wasn't up at the crack of dawn, exercising .....working until 10 pm ..... doing paperwork .....planning ...... and more planning.

I felt I had to put 100% into everything I did, and that anyone who didn't throw themselves into whatever they did just wasn't doing it well. I would write lists of what I had/wanted to achieve that day or that week and feel mightily dissatisfied if I didn't achieve it all. Since I started practising Mindfulness I have found less need for lists. Having made room in my head for the more important things in my life I find that these get done as a matter of course. By spending less time frantically trying to get everything done and not achieving much I have found that it all gets done in the end.

The rush in my life has gone. I no longer have to speed everywhere .... and, this I have only just realised as I am writing about it. That is what happens with Mindfulness, it subversively sneaks into your life, influencing it in a good way until, like I have just realised, you find that you are doing things differently and thereby getting different and better results. By having this effect on your life, you find you feel less guilty about the quiet times, the times when you can sit quietly and eat your meal. That you don't have to stay up half the night finishing paperwork because in your now calm state you have made time, the right amount of time to do it before then.

Sometimes I notice tension in my body, so I just pause and it goes away.

Middle age spread

'The only way to keep your health is to eat what you don't want, drink what you don't like, and do what you'd rather not.' Mark Twain

We all have heard of the saying - breakfast like a king, lunch like a prince, dine like a pauper. There have been numerous studies to support and refute this theory and as we are all different then what suits one may not suit another. But the thing to remember is that you have a choice, if your old way of living isn't sitting as well as it did then there is a reason, and as to a certain extent, as you are what you eat, this may be your starting point to feeling better.

The old excuse that it is only age that is causing your middle age spread or it's the menopause is nonsense as far as I am concerned. As I say to my Pilates students, I can help you get a flatter stomach but only if you stop putting food in your mouth. You won't gain pounds if you don't over consume the calories. If it was just age and menopause that made older people fat then everyone over the age of 60 would be, but they are not. There are those who have never had a weight problem and there are those who have chosen to keep active and to readjust their eating habits to suit their changing lifestyles.

But we always have wine with our dinner, we always have a dessert, I always have sugar in my tea, we always have cake or biscuits with our afternoon coffee .... That's great and no-one is judging you for that but if you are starting to complain about not being able to reach your shoes laces or that your acid reflux is keeping you up at night then surely that is the time to examine what you are doing to cause or exacerbate the situation. And as I have already said, you don't have to be deprived of all life's goodies but be mindful of what you eat and when. That may be all it takes rather than a lifetime of abstinence.

I refuse to let menopause be an excuse for putting on weight.

Going forward

'A healthy attitude is contagious but don't wait to catch it from others. Be a carrier.' Tom Stoppard

Sometimes, I have found it is about choosing what you want to do in a day, and like a good recipe, adding the right amount of exercise, the right amount of good nourishing food, the right amount of a job or work you enjoy and the right amount of 'me' time. The minute you say you haven't got time for this or that then you have sabotaged your own efforts. It takes very little time and effort to make time for yourself. I was talking to a young girl recently who is totally lost, feels she has no choices in any area of her life at the moment. So I suggested that if she achieved nothing else today, she could at least try to buy herself something to eat that she really would enjoy and not beat herself up about later.

We often look for big things to make the changes, tip the scales, but as with most things in life, the most sustainable things in life are the small things. These are the underpinnings for the bigger buildings. I never negate a small action or deed because all those little positive nuggets sooner or later amount up to something big. And these are the positive steps we can take while waiting for the really great stuff to arrive. But what you might actually find, as I did and still do, is that the small stuff can often be as big and shiny and influential and motivating as the 'perceived' big prize.

So it may appear from what I have said, that I have most things sussed in my life. Well some days I do and some days I don't and such is life. I think it would be boring if it all went well all the time, it is the challenges that help us to grow rather than get stuck in that safe rut out of the sunshine, then shrivel and die. Things that stay the same may appear safe but they lose their lustre. You may not believe it but if you only ate your favourite chocolate every day you would soon get so used to its flavour that if you were being mindful, you would tire of it and crave a contrast.

I don't get it right every day, but these days I get it more right than wrong.

A Mindful future

'Too often in life, something happens and we blame other people for us not being happy or satisfied or fulfilled. So the point is, we all have choices, and we make the choice to accept people or situations or to not accept situations.' Tom Brady

I feel we change and evolve as we go through our lives and there are always adjustments to be made. With regard to our food, we need to change our intake and nutrients in accordance with where we are. I am always reassessing what sort of food is most beneficial for me on a daily, monthly and yearly basis depending on where I am and what I am doing. I will continue to vary what I eat and address any nutritional needs as I go. As we get older we tend to need less food. I think a lot of older people put on weight not just because of their age but because they either eat the same as they used to or eat more socially as they have more spare time and at the same time move less.

To my mind, leading a Mindful life increases your options, gives you an awareness of the choices you have, reminding you that you do have choices and thereby opening up a whole new perspective on life. I intend continuing to practise and explore all the possibilities that this new life skill is bringing me. The one thing I was looking for and I know from talking to people, many of them want the same, is peace. Nothing more grand or exciting than that. Being a relatively new convert to Mindfulness I have started to have glimpses of this peacefulness which can appear under the surface even during the most trying of situations.

You know that whatever you are doing, whether it is eating, working, socialising or whatever, when it is underpinned by a deep sense of peacefulness, your activity takes on a whole different feel. Sometimes when I am writing this stuff, it all sounds a bit 'new age' and airy fairy but it's not. Ask anyone who knows me, ethereal I'm not but I much prefer the way I feel now to the 'bull in a china shop' I was not so long ago. I used to worry that if I meditated and did all that calm stuff, that I would lose my edge, not achieve all the things I want to achieve, to live life to the full. But actually, I am still living life to the full, but I am enjoying it at a level I never experienced before.

I have never felt more peaceful, happy and well in my whole life.

Improving your relationship with food

When you are relaxed and calm, when you feel in control of your life then willpower becomes a by product. Struggling to have willpower disempowers you and weakens your resolve.

If you can breathe you can move. There are no excuses for not doing some form of exercise. Our bodies are designed to move. The sense of wellbeing you get is motivating.

It may be a slog at first, but five minutes a day will grow into ten .... What is the alternative .... Anything at all is better than nothing.

Remember the life balance - too much of anything will burn you out. Then you will revert back to making bad food choices because you are exhausted.

I regularly see people with various aches and pains, or constant bad backs - well I am sorry but if you weren't overweight your body would have less cause to complain.

How can you put on weight in 'middle age' or after menopause if you don't put the food in your mouth? You don't get fat on fresh air, you get fat by buying into the media portrayal of the symptoms of old age. Prove them wrong.

Rethink your day or life regularly. What didn't work yesterday change? Take a different approach. If you can't change the what, change the how.

Be Mindful every day of your actions so that at the end of the day you have made conscious decisions at every point and nothing was taken for granted. Then go to sleep with a smile, knowing you did the best for you.

Every morning is a new day, a new chapter in your life. How do you want your day to go. What do you want to include in your day. What food will you eat that will really excite you.

Never underestimate the value of rest and sleep. We are a cocktail of many things - work, play, rest, meditation or just being. The more you nurture yourself the more you will have left to give to others

10. And Finally... Willpower

Use it or lose it
Later maybe
Stop beating yourself up
In conclusion

And Finally... Willpower

'Willpower is the key to success. Successful people strive no matter what they feel by applying their will to overcome apathy, doubt or fear' Dan Millman

I finished writing this book while on the idyllic island of Koh Phangan in Thailand. On the way back we were delayed for three hours at Bangkok airport. It was here that I discovered a book called Willpower by Roy F. Baumeister and John Tierney. I was so grateful that it was a long flight home as it enabled me to read the book from cover to cover. I soon had my pen to hand highlighting all the pertinent points. To my great delight, many of the things they said I had said in my book. But while theirs was a result of studies by psychologists, mine has come mainly from life experience.

I would like to share with you some of the most useful and inspiring points that they covered. I finished the book feeling totally inspired and excited by much of what they said. It made so much sense and what a useful tool for understanding why our willpower is such an elusive thing. The first thing they suggest is that willpower, as most of us know, is not an infinite thing. Sometimes we have it and sometimes it just disappears. We can wake up in the morning with it in abundance, but by mid-afternoon it has deserted us completely. I would like you to imagine it as a large glass tube full of coloured liquid. After a good night's sleep you wake up and the tube is full.

The authors suggest, and the studies support the idea that as the day goes on your willpower is drained by events in your day. Even things like thinking negatively, resisting temptation, feeling stressed, having to make decisions can have a draining effect on your willpower. So no wonder most of us, find at the end of the day our tube of willpower is down to the dregs. They found that one of the contributing factors to willpower diminishing is low blood sugar. As willpower is a brain function, a deficit in glucose will affect your ability to keep on track. Now before you start equating blood sugar and glucose with chocolate, they suggest that protein is the key.

I am continuously making positive choices throughout my day. Nothing in my life is there by chance.

Use it or lose it

'Strength does not come from physical capacity. It comes from an indomitable will' Mahatma Gandhi

It would appear to be quite a balancing act. Willpower is strengthened like a muscle by exercising it. However if by exercising it you have to resist temptation, this will deplete your willpower. They also found that those who were better at having willpower went on to achieve better in life. It doesn't matter what you exercise willpower over initially, you will in the end be able to have self-control in any area of your life. So if in the beginning you find it impossible to manage your eating issues, try a different approach. Find another area of your life you would like to improve. Something less challenging. It doesn't matter. Once you improve your willpower in that area, your willpower overall will be strengthened.

One thing they suggest you don't do, and I am as guilty of this as the rest, is having a whole list of things you want to change. No-one has enough willpower for a list. Have only one focus and when that becomes a habit and you have incorporated it successfully into your life then you can focus on the next thing. But as I have said previously, the other things you want to change or achieve should follow automatically because you now know how to harness and control yourself and your life.

I was very interested to read in the book about Abraham Lincoln who spent his whole life striving to be a better person. He acknowledged the fact that he couldn't improve everything he wanted to all at once. He made a chart and listed several characteristics about himself he wanted to improve. Every day he marked the chart next to any aspect he had been able address. He did not worry about the ones he was not successful with, his aim was to have at least one line of complete crosses alongside one of his aims for the whole week. I loved this idea. Trying to achieve everything at once is depleting but finding a sense of achievement and focus by even being successful in one area takes the pressure off being all things to all men and coming up short, thereby feeling disempowered and demotivated.

I get pleasure out of everything I do. Even chores.

Later maybe...

'Willpower is trying very hard not to do something you want to do very much' John Ortberg

As I sat on the plane reading, being inspired, the air hostess brought round ice creams. I wasn't hungry but I took one anyway. I opened it mindlessly and as it was too hard to scoop out I left it. To my great delight, I decided I no longer had any desire to eat it. This was amazing and something that they advocated in the book. Our brains like completion of tasks or projects. It is almost like closure. If something remains unresolved we will be niggled and niggled until we take some sort of action.

Like that biscuit sitting on the side beckoning to you. If you try to resist it, fighting temptation with all your might, your willpower will weaken. If however you say to yourself I will have it later, you have flagged up an action and your brain is happy.

It is like the urge surfing of the earlier chapter. What the research found was that deciding to allow yourself to have it later operates in the mind a bit like having it now. And they found that by doing this, if at a later stage you did have the treat you actually wanted less of it.

It would appear that denying yourself the treat increases the craving but the promise of it later diminishes the desire. It takes willpower to refuse a treat. It is however apparently less stressful and depleting on the mind to say later rather than never. Added to this sense of self control is the anticipation of the pleasure to come rather than acting on the impulse or craving as it arose.

I can now look at the chocolate and crisp aisles and think 'don't fancy any of that'.

Stop beating yourself up...

'The more things you do, the more you can do' Lucille Ball

So if we wake up with a full tank of willpower, how can we stop it from evaporating completely as we go through our day? One way is to be aware of our nutrition. Giving yourself permission to eat rather than struggling with constant denial. This will turn into a vicious circle. The more you resist temptation the more willpower you spend and the more willpower you spend the harder it will be to resist temptation. Be aware however that while boosting your blood sugar is desirable, what you boost it with is important too. Imagine you are feeding your race horse. You could win a lot of money if the horse completes the course. If you feed it nutrient deficient food it will not last the course, but if you feed it protein, you strengthen its resolve to win.

Another thing to be aware of, is how much you want to achieve in the day. If like me, you have a hundred and one things to do you will soon run out of steam as you strive to do it all. Do yourself a favour. Aim to be realistic. What is really important for you to do? You never get everything done anyway so why give yourself a hard time and pile the pressure on when you know at the end of the day you won't do it all. And then what? Demoralised, all out of willpower, you throw in the towel on another frustrating day. Acknowledge that the more things you have on your list the more drained your willpower will be. Choose three things and get them done effortlessly and well, then anything else is a bonus. At the end of the day you can say, 'look what I have achieved' rather than 'I didn't do this or that'.

There appear to be so many things we do subconsciously that it is no wonder we fail at controlling our eating. The authors suggest that 'bad habits are strengthened by routine'. I understand this totally as I have struggled with not eating when I get in late at night from work. I have in the past gone straight into the kitchen, put the kettle on and reached for the Ryvita tin. They say that changing your routine makes it easier to break these unhelpful habits. I myself, now go straight to bed. Getting more sleep is one of my lifestyle improvement aims. It now has the double benefit of controlling my night time binges too. And thereby by being less tired my willpower is not so depleted, and my self-control is stronger.

All areas of my life have improved since practising Mindfulness.

In conclusion...

'To assert your willpower is simply to make up your mind that you want something, and then refuse to be put off' Phillip Cooper

I for one, am not a good loser. I really don't want to spend the rest of my life doing battle with my waistband. I want to channel my time and energies into other more rewarding things. I don't want my thoughts to be overwhelmed by what to eat, when to eat, what I shouldn't be eating and hating myself for failing again and again and again. I like the feeling of being slim and fit and healthy. There are many things in our lives that we have less control over but eating is not one of them. We can choose what we put in our mouths, why and when.

These days we have so many choices in our lives, so many temptations it is no wonder we struggle to find balance. I like the idea of a breathing space .... Mindfulness can give you that ...... If you are struggling to cope with something or resisting temptation ...... just give yourself a breathing space ...... stop, relax, clear your mind ..... even for a couple of seconds or minutes...... give yourself the chance to act rather than react ....then you can choose the best course of action for you.

Just by changing how you do one thing, whether it is buying a smaller packet of crisps, saving your treat until later, distracting yourself and then deciding if you still want to take that course of action, anything, any small thing you change will be like dropping a pebble into a pool, the ripple effect will change your life. It is like changing your course, your direction, your path. Just a one degree change will take you in another direction.   And you may well end up exactly where you wanted to be.

I believe I am what I choose to eat.

Improving your relationship with food

Bear in mind you have a finite amount of Willpower at the beginning of everyday. Be Mindful of what you use it on.

Your Willpower muscle can be strengthened by using it and nourishing it.

Pick your battles. One challenge a day is enough. One project successfully completed is enough. One temptation successfully overcome is enough.

Give yourself credit for what you did achieve. Forgive yourself and let go of what you didn't. Tomorrow is another day. Another full tank of Willpower.

Delay gratification rather than denial. Promise yourself to have it or do it later. Then maybe you will or maybe you won't.

Anticipation of a pleasure is often as tasty as the pleasure itself.

Limit your to do list. A long list not done is disempowering. A short list well done is empowering.

Changing your habits rather than culling them will give you a different result.

Improve your relationship with food by demoting its place in your life. There are so many other things you could be spending your time and creative energy on.

Nothing changes if nothing changes .....

How to meditate

'Don't seek, don't search, don't ask, don't knock, don't demand - relax. If you relax, it comes, if you relax, it is there, if you relax you start vibrating with it' Osho

When I started I tried with the breathing, focussing on my breath and I would find that even before the end of the first in and out breath my mind had wandered. I would drag it back and another thought would worm its way into my mind. Often when trying to clear my mind, it would feel like I had a bag of ferrets in my head as all my suppressed thoughts fought for supremacy. It took many times for me to get to a stage where I could keep my mind reasonably clear for more than two seconds. What I found worked for me was to start by feeling my face. I would close my eyes and feel the sensation of my eyebrows; if they were tense then I would stay with them until they were relaxed.

Then I would focus on my eyes and eye sockets. I found these were often more tense than my eyebrows and it took practise to mentally smooth them out. The last area was my jaw, when you relax your jaw, your neck, shoulders and whole body begins to melt. While I was doing this I was unable to think, then I could focus on my breathing. If I then found my mind starting to wander I would go back to feeling my face. Once I got better at this I began to feel wonderfully calm and peaceful in my body. I felt light with no tension. The sensation is so nice that I try for five minutes several times a day, it's like a tonic.

I find that Mindful meditation is like a sanctuary, a place to go if my day gets challenging or if some thought starts to dominate my mind. I don't even have to be sat somewhere to do this. Sometimes when I am driving and I need to calm my mind or clear my head I just focus on the sensations of my face and I find the source of my discourse dissolves, dilutes and disappears. I can honestly say I have many less thoughts than I used to and feel so much more peaceful. It does however take practise and consistency.

Books that have inspired me:

The Power is Within you - *Louise Hay*

The Power of Now - *Elkhart tolle*

The Secret - *Rhonda Byrne*

The Book of Secrets - *Deepak Chopra*

The Law of Attraction - *Esther and Jerry hicks*

Willpower - *Roy F. Baumeister & John Tierney*

Sex is not compulsory - *Liz Hodgkinson*

The Way of the Warrior - *Dan Millman*

All of the books - *Paulo Coelho*

The Time Keeper - *Mitch Albom*

The Art of Happiness - *Dalai Lama*

Feel the Fear and do it anyway - *Susan Jeffries*

How to get from where you are to where you want to be - *Jack Canfield*

Having it all - *John Assaraf*

How to get what you want and want what you have - *John Gray*

Men are from Mars and Women are from Venus - *John Gray*

Sex Life - *Dr Pamela Stephenson-Connelly*

I can make you thin - *Paul McKenna*

The Game of Life and how to play it - *Florence Scovel Shinn*

How to think more about sex - *Alain de Botton*